MEGAN KEARNEY'S

BEAUTY
AND THE BEAST
THE

For Nick,
who broke the curse

Beauty and The Beast: Act One
Copyright © 2014 Megan Kearney

Published by The Quietly
First Canadian Edition

Library and Archives Canada Cataloguing in Publication

Kearney, Megan, 1986-, author, illustrator
Megan Kearney's Beauty and The Beast. Act one.

Based on the works of Gabrielle-Suzanne Barbot de Villeneuve
and Jeanne-Marie Leprince de Beaumont.
Includes bibliographical references.

ISBN 978-0-9937212-0-5 (pbk.)

1. Graphic novels. I. Title. II. Title: Beauty and The Beast.
Act one.

PN6733.K42M42 2014   741.5'971   C2014-902234-4

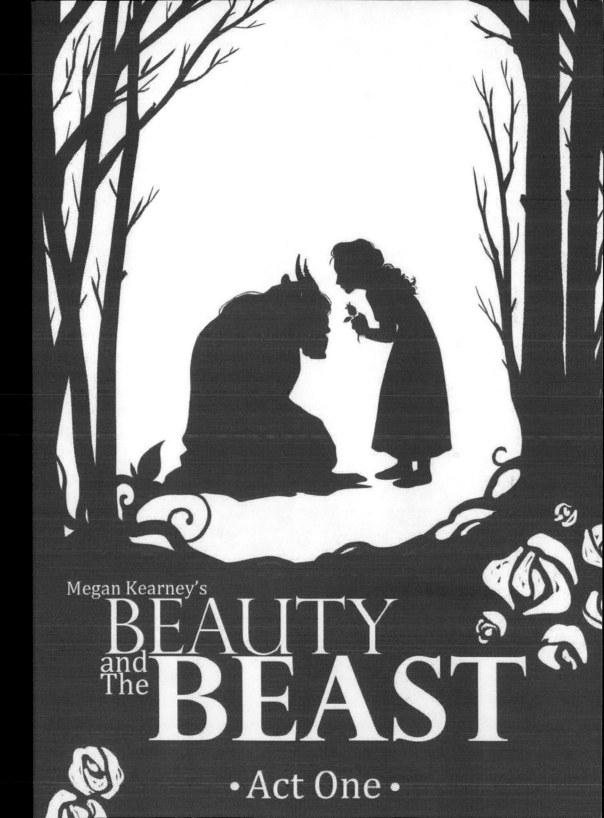

Megan Kearney's

BEAUTY
and The BEAST

• Act One •

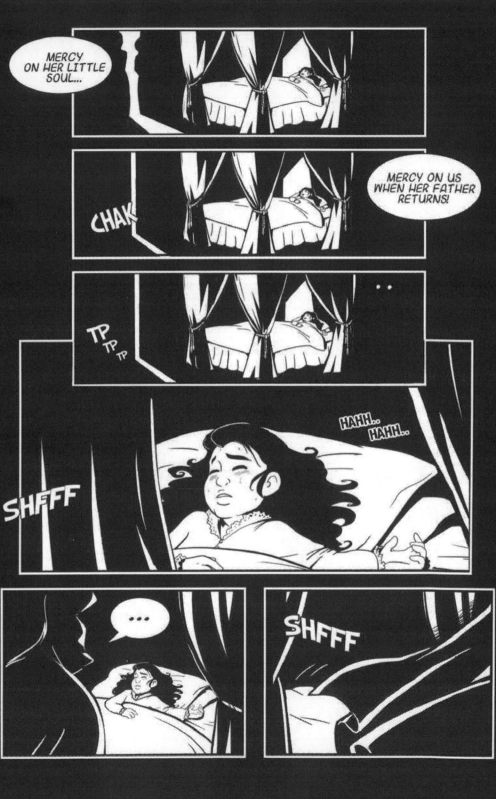

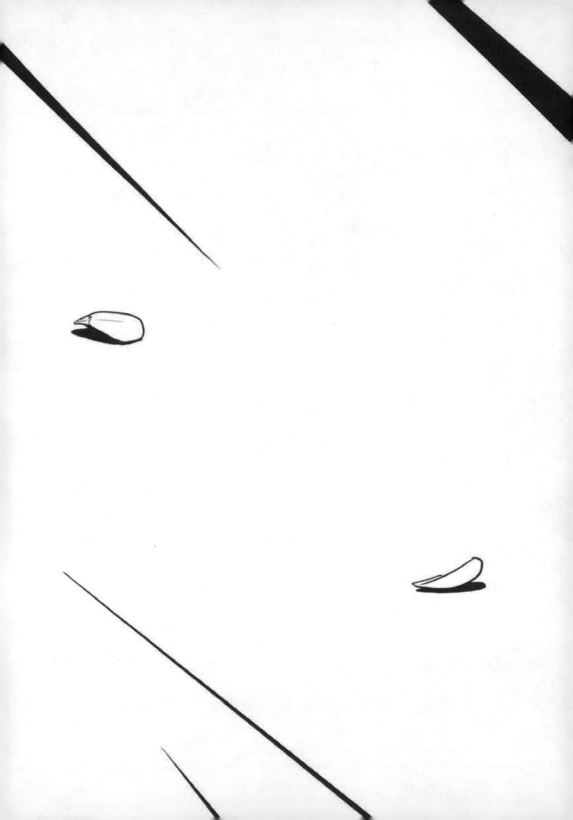

•ACT ONE•
CHAPTER ONE

catchfly, cinquefoil, cardamom

Verbena, Grass, Flowering Almond

•ACT ONE•
CHAPTER THREE

Coriander, Calycanthus, Sweet Alyssum,

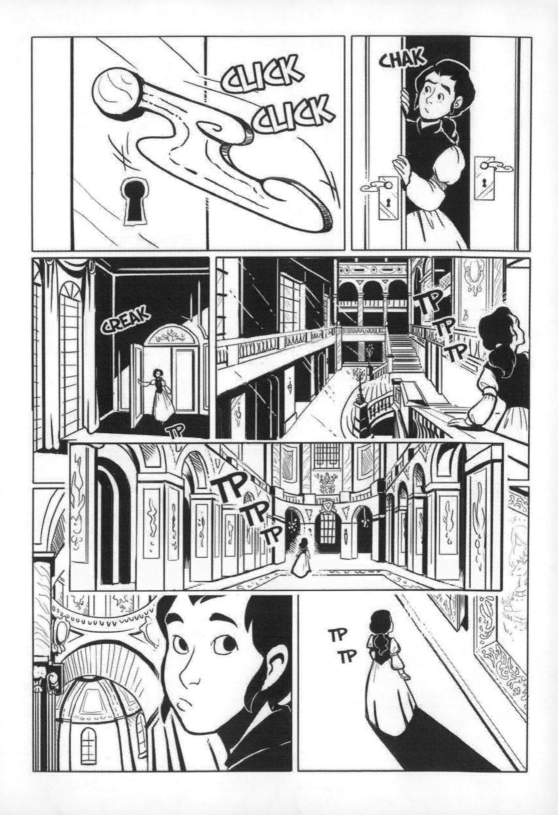

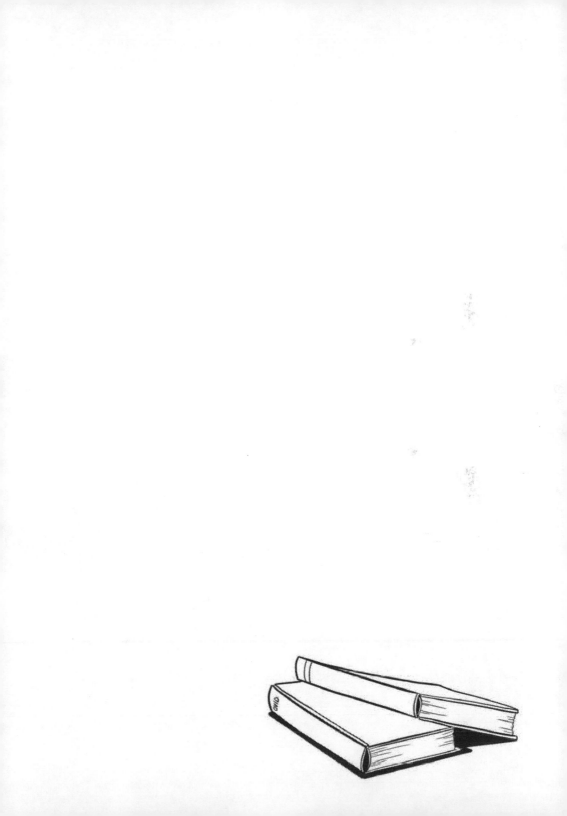

•ACT ONE•
CHAPTER FOUR

Snowdrop, periwinkle, bindweed

•ACT ONE•
CHAPTER FIVE

Dragon's Wort, Broken Cornstraw, Frog Ophrys

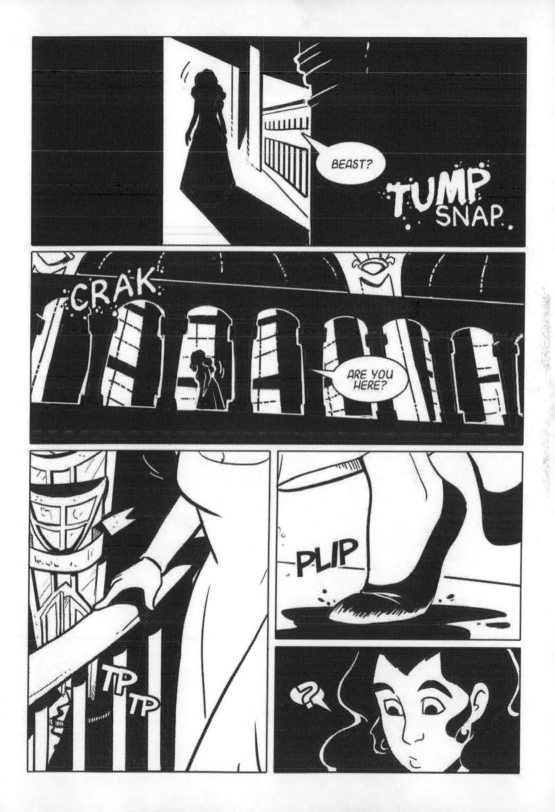

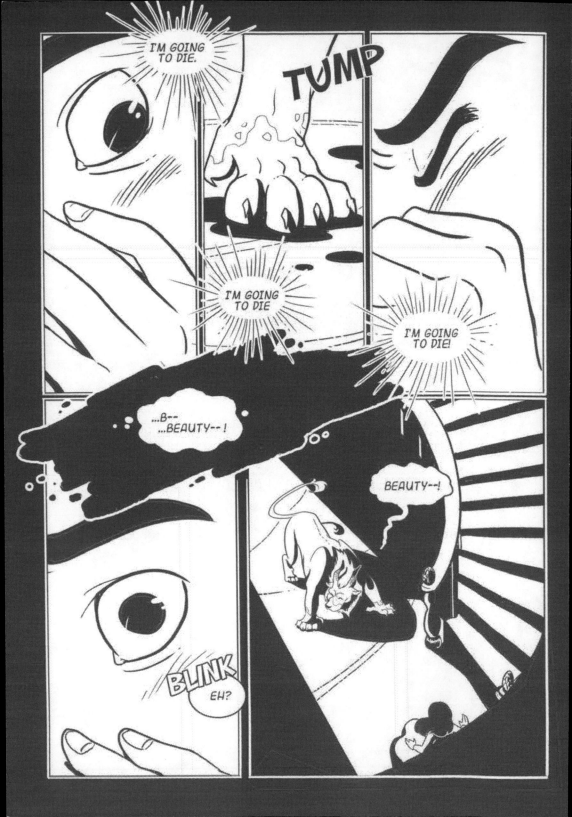

• Liner Notes •

The Story of Beauty and the Beast

During the reign of Louis XIV, it was the vogue for educated noblewomen, and some men, to gather and spin fairy tales together. The conte de fées told in these salons laid the foundation of the literary fairy tale, a very different creature than the earlier folk narratives from which they sprang.

The Story of Beauty and the Beast first appeared under this name in 1740, and was written by Gabrielle-Suzanne Barbot Gallon de Villeneuve, a French noblewoman. Villeneuve based her ornate narrative on a number of other fairy tales and myths, reaching all the way back to ancient Greece. Her sly critique of society, marriage and politics gives the novel flair, but its length and propensity towards great detail did not guarantee it immortality.

How then, are we still telling and retelling her tale? The version of Beauty and the Beast most people are familiar with today is based on a much shorter adaptation of Villeneuve's lengthy story, published by governess Jeanne-Marie Leprince de Beaumont. Beaumont stripped the story down to its bare bones, eliminating subplots, extraneous details, and all save a handful of characters. Her simple and moralistic retelling was published in **Le Magasin des Enfants** in 1757 and was one of the first fairy tales specifically aimed at children.

Beauty and the Beast has enjoyed great popularity throughout its life, consistantly ranking among the most well-known fairy tales. It has been adapted to film many times, most notably by Jean Cocteau in 1946, Juraj Herz in 1978 and by the Walt Disney Company in 1991. Numerous stage adaptations, including ballet and opera, have been performed, and many authors have drawn on the themes of Beauty and the Beast both explicitly and implicilty.

What has made Beauty and The Beast such an enduring narrative? The power of the tale may come from its potent imagery and ever-evolving meaning. What was first penned as a story discussing arranged marriage has mutated and grown with each retelling, finding relevance in many contexts and social climates. It continues to change and rearrange itself today.

Just as the women of Louis XIV's court spoke of their lives through fairy tales, we continue to look at ourselves through a lense of fiction, exploring the human condition through the metaphor of beastliness, seeking the beauty that we hope resides at the heart of ourselves.

The Language of Flowers

ommunicating sentiments through bouquets coded in the Language of Flowers is an old tradition that was most recently popular in Victorian England. However, sweethearts around the world have been exchanging covert flirtations with flowers at least as far back as the Ottoman Empire. Many books have been written on the subject, and almost as many different meanings have been assigned to popular plants and flowers! For the purposes of this book, the following interpretations may be inferred.

Bindweed- uncertainty
Broken Cornstraw- disagreement
Calycanthus- benevolence
Cardamom - a father's error
Catchfly - a snare
Cinquefoil- a beloved daughter
Coriander- hidden merit
Dragonswort- horror
Flowering Almond- hope
Frog Ophrys- disgust
Grass- submission
Periwinkle- early recollections
Snowdrop - consolation
Sweet alyssum- worth beyond beauty
Verbena - enchantment, honesty

Acknowledgements

This book could not have been completed without the aid of some very wonderful, very patient people. I can't possibly name all the individuals who have emerged as part of the wonderful community this comic has introduced me to, but I owe a special debt of gratitude to the following folks:

Laura Neubert, for her encyclopedia-like knowledge of the story and her willingness to act as editor even as her own deadlines loomed large

Meaghan Carter and Sanya Anwar, for a seemingly endless stream of snarkiness and reminders that it's fine.

The ladies of High Tea at the Embassy, for stocking the studio tea cupboard and for the monthly dose of sympathy and goodwill that keeps me going

Tom Lay, for swooping in at the last minute with layout help

My Dear Readers, who have followed Beauty and The Beast online since its launch, providing me with hours of joy and amusement and some great crackpot theories about just what is going on in that Castle

Nick Hendriks, who encouraged me to take this seriously, and whose support, faith, and great patience has made it possible for me to continue doing so.

Megan Kearney is a recovering Navy Brat,
raised with a healthy love of books and an
unhealthy love of comics and cartoons. She
graduated from the University of Windsor
with a degree in Visual Arts and an English
Minor and went straight on to Sheridan College
where she earned an Honours degree in
Animation. She lives in Toronto with her
husband and an indeterminate number
of rabbits.

Made in the USA
Lexington, KY
31 May 2014